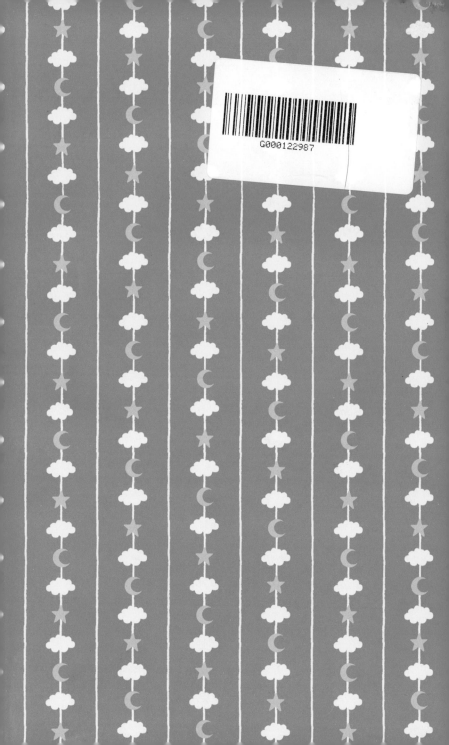

Jacqueline Wilson

ILLUSTRATED BY NICK SHARRATT

Dream Journal

DOUBLEDAY

MY DREAMS!

Children often ask me where I get my ideas from when
I write my stories. I usually say that I don't really know
how I do it. Ideas just seem to pop into my head. I say
that it's a bit like when you dream. You can't really
decide when to have a dream. It just happens, whether
you want it to or not. Sometimes it's a dream that seems
very real, and it's a mixed-up version of something
that's really happened. Sometimes it's completely bizarre
and strange and magical and you have no idea how
it floated into your head.

I wonder if you have vivid dreams? I find I have
extraordinary dreams, but nowadays I have to write them
down the moment I wake up or else they drift away in
my thoughts and I can barely remember them.

I have such difficulty remembering the dreams I had last
night and yet I can clearly remember some dreams I
had as a child. I didn't sleep terribly well when I was little.
I sometimes had the most awful nightmares. The worst
kind were when people were chasing me and I'd think
I'd woken up and was safe, but then they'd poke an
arm through the wall and grab me out of my bed.
I'd know that I was back in the nightmare and I'd
try so hard to open my eyes to escape.

That's one of the drawbacks of having an overactive imagination! However, I had beautiful childhood dreams too. I didn't often dream about flying but I had many weird and wonderful swimming  dreams when I glided effortlessly along silvery rivers in the moonlight.

Do you think dreams ever come true? I don't think they necessarily do, but one or two of my recurring dreams do seem to have come true. I've dreamt about a big and beautiful house full of books on and off throughout my life – and now I'm actually living in that dream house. I also dreamt as a child that I was in some huge hall, standing on a stage, addressing a vast audience. It felt very strange and exciting. I couldn't believe so many people wanted to see and hear me. Whenever I give a talk about my books in a big venue now, I remember that dream and smile.

I do hope you enjoy keeping this special journal. Sweet dreams!

Jacqueline Wilson

THIS DREAM JOURNAL BELONGS TO:

Here's a
photo of me!

Name:_____

Address:_____

_____

_____

_____

_____

Phone number:_____

_____

Email:_____

_____

MY BEST DREAM!

You'll have thousands of dreams throughout your life, but what's your favourite dream so far? It might be about something you're desperate to happen in real life: becoming a famous actress or singer, swimming with dolphins, or writing a brilliant book! Or it might be even more magical: you might be able to fly in your dream, turn into an animal, or have incredible powers.

Write all about your best dream here, or draw a picture.

MARTY SAYS: You could even design a comic, all about what happened in your dream! My best dreams are always about my very own superhero, Mighty Mart.

MY WORST DREAM!

You won't remember every dream you've ever had –
and there are some you might wish you could forget.
Everyone has scary, worrying or sad dreams sometimes.
What's the worst dream you've ever had?

Jot it all down here, or draw a picture. Sharing or
talking about something that has made you unhappy
can often help you to feel much better about it.
You might even be able to laugh about it!

VIOLET SAYS: Write down three words
that describe your dream. I've given
you some examples – these are words
that describe a bad dream I once had.

Terrifying Ghostly Spooky

MY STRANGEST DREAM!

All sorts of things can happen in dreams that would
never take place in real life, so they can sometimes
be very strange indeed. Dreams often make no sense
when you stop to think about them! What's the
weirdest dream you've ever had?

You can write about it here, or sketch some
of the oddest bits of the dream.

ANDREA SAYS: Hmm . . . I wonder
what Radish dreams about?

MY FUNNIEST DREAM!

Have you ever woken up from a dream with a big smile on your face? You might even have been chuckling to yourself! It's lovely when that happens, and probably means you've had a very funny dream!

Describe the funniest dream you can remember having. Why not ask your best friends what their own funniest dreams are, and add them all to this page?

ELSA SAYS: Why did the little boy take a bar of chocolate to bed? So that he would have sweet dreams!

DREAMS IN JACQUELINE WILSON'S BOOKS

Lots of the characters in Jacqueline's books have
memorable dreams. Here are just a few of them . . .

TRACY'S DREAM

There wasn't much point in getting to sleep, because when
I did eventually nod off I just had these stupid nightmares.
It's as if there's a video inside my head and it switches
itself on the minute my eyes close and I keep hoping it's
going to be showing this great comedy that'll have me in
stitches but then the creepy music starts and I know I'm
in for it. Last night was the Great Horror Movie of all
time. I was stuck in the dark somewhere and there was
something really scary coming up quick behind me so I
had to run like mad. Then I got to this big round pool and
there were these stepping stones with people perching on
them and I jumped on to the first one and there was no
room at all because that fat Aunty Peggy was spread all
over it. I tried to cling to her but she gave me a big smack
and sent me flying. So then I jumped on to the next
stepping stone and Julie and Ted were there and I tried
to grab hold of them but they just turned their backs

on me and didn't even try to catch me when I fell and so I had to try to reach the next stepping stone but I was in the water doing my doggy-paddle and it was getting harder and harder, and every time I swam to a stepping stone all these people prodded at me with sticks and pushed me away and I kept going under the water and . . .

. . . And then I woke up and I know that whenever I dream about water it spells Trouble with a capital T. I had to make my own dash to the airing cupboard and the laundry basket. I was unfortunate enough to bump into Justine too. She didn't look as if she'd slept much either. Her eyes seemed a bit on the red side. I couldn't help feeling a bit mean then, in spite of everything. So I gave her this big smile and I said, 'I'm sorry about what happened to your alarm clock, Justine.'

FROM *THE STORY OF TRACY BEAKER*

MANDY'S DREAM

I started pretending. OK, I wasn't boring, baby, goody-goody Mandy White. I was . . . Miranda Rainbow. I was cool. I was colourful. I wore loads of make-up and had this ultra-hip hairstyle. I wore the most amazing super sexy clothes. I had pierced ears and a stud in my nose. I didn't have a mum. I didn't have a dad. I lived all by myself in this incredible modern flat. Sometimes my friends stayed overnight at my place. I had heaps of friends and they all begged me to be their best friend.

I fell asleep being Miranda Rainbow but then Mum woke me up tucking the covers over me and I couldn't get back to sleep for ages.

FROM *BAD GIRLS*

❦ ELSIE'S DREAM ❦

Sometimes I almost forgot that Nan was stuck in the sanatorium. Whenever I dreamed of her she was at home, sitting in her armchair sucking pear drops or fast asleep in bed with her mouth open, her teeth grinning in a glass beside her.

I wondered if she dreamed of me. Maybe we could somehow jump into each other's dreams? I went to sleep thinking of Nan. I dreamed that we walked hand in hand all the way to London – no cough, no limps, the two of us striding out, singing 'God Save the Queen'. When we got there, it was terribly crowded. We were pushed here and jostled there, but Nan kept tight hold of my hand and helped me climb right up some railings. We balanced there, and cheered when the Queen went past in her golden coach pulled by eight grey horses. They all tossed their heads and neighed at us, and then the Queen herself stuck her head out of the window and shouted, 'Hello, Nan, hello, Elsie! Thank you for coming!' while the crowd roared.

It was such a wonderful dream I told it to the others at breakfast time, but they laughed at me.

'You're absolutely bonkers, Gobface. As if the Queen would ever talk to you!' said Martin, chortling.

FROM *QUEENIE*

ALL ABOUT DREAMS!

DID YOU KNOW . . .

For every ten dreams we have, we forget
nine and only remember one!

DID YOU KNOW . . .

Our brains can't invent people's faces, so you
might wake up thinking you have dreamed about
a stranger, but in actual fact you must have seen
that person in real life and forgotten about them.
They might be someone you sat next to on the bus
last week, or walked past in the street three years
ago – but they are real, not imagined.

DID YOU KNOW . . .

You might not realize it, but on average, people
have between four and six dreams every night!

DID YOU KNOW . . .

In Ancient Rome, some dreams were presented
to the Emperor to be discussed. Lots of people believed
dreams were messages from the gods and goddesses.

DID YOU KNOW . . .

Not everyone dreams in full colour.
Some people dream in black and white!

DID YOU KNOW . . .

One of the most common things people
dream about is teeth! Lots of people believe
that if your teeth fall out in a dream, it means
you are feeling worried or anxious about
something in real life. Others believe a dream
about losing teeth means you're about to
come in to some money!

DID YOU KNOW . . .

Babies don't dream about themselves
until they are around three.

DID YOU KNOW . . .

Animals dream too! If you've ever watched a dog
sleeping, you might have noticed its paws moving,
as if it's running along chasing something.

PUZZLE TIME!

WORDSEARCH

All these words are to do with dreams, sleeping or night-time. Can you find them all? Good luck!

Teddy

Moon

Flying

Stars

Teeth

Pyjamas

Sleep

B	T	P	Y	J	A	M	A	S
J	D	A	E	G	M	F	X	L
N	I	G	H	T	M	A	R	E
W	D	N	M	E	A	O	R	E
O	C	I	E	D	W	C	O	P
L	C	Y	M	D	A	O	S	N
L	V	L	O	Y	G	C	W	C
I	Q	F	R	I	O	P	E	K
P	Z	U	Y	B	N	T	E	L
F	D	W	I	S	R	A	T	S
T	E	E	T	H	H	O	O	E
N	A	I	B	U	H	R	S	N

Pillow

Memory

Bed

Cocoa

Sweet

Nightmare

☁ LETTER CHALLENGE ☁

How many words can you make from these letters?
Give yourself and your friends five minutes each, and
then count them up. For every two-letter word, you
score two points, for every three-letter word, you score
three points, and so on. Whoever has the most points
wins! There are two examples to help start you off:

SWEET DREAMS

Team   Draw

FAMOUS DREAMS

• Mary Shelley's novel *Frankenstein* was inspired
by a dream, while Robert Louis Stevenson
said the idea for *Dr Jekyll and Mr Hyde*
also came to him in a dream.

• The famous comic artist Hergé was having horrible
nightmares set in a snowy white landscape.
He was advised to take a rest from making comics
but instead decided to start a new one, using the
landscape from his dreams. He ended up writing
Tintin in Tibet, which was one of the most successful
comics ever – and his nightmares stopped completely!

• The melody for one of the most famous songs
ever written, *Yesterday* by the Beatles, popped
into Paul McCartney's head in a dream.
When he woke up, he thought he had just
remembered a song from his childhood –
but it was actually brand-new.

IMPORTANT ADDRESSES AND PHONE NUMBERS

Name: _____

Address: _____

_____

_____

_____

Phone number: _____

Email: _____

Name: _____

Address: _____

_____

_____

_____

Phone number: _____

Email: _____

Name: _____

Address: _____

_____

_____

_____

Phone number: _____

Email: _____

Name: _____

Address: _____

_____

_____

_____

Phone number: _____

Email: _____

Name: _____

Address: _____

_____

_____

_____

Phone number: _____

Email: _____

Name: _____

Address: _____

_____

_____

_____

Phone number: _____

Email: _____

Name: _____

Address: _____

_____

_____

_____

Phone number: _____

Email: _____

Name: _____

Address: _____

_____

_____

_____

Phone number: _____

Email: _____

JANUARY

'Oh, Madame Adeline, may I come and live with you?' I said.

'Of course, my precious child!' she said, clasping me close, smelling wonderfully of sweetmeats and roses. She wrapped me tightly in her train. 'Indeed, you are my child, my own dear long-lost daughter, and now we will live together for ever. You are not really called Hetty Feather. I named you—'

'Hetty! Hetty!'

It was Jem, tugging me.

'Stop it, Jem,' I said furiously, struggling to stay in my wondrous dream.

HETTY FEATHER

January 1

January 2

January 3

January 4

January 5

January 6

January 7

January 8

January 9

January 10

January 11

January 12

January 13

January 14

January 15

January 16

January 17

January 18

January 19

January 20

January 21

January 22

January 23

January 24

January 25

January 26

January 27

January 28

January 29

January 30

January 31

Notes

MY JANUARY DREAMS

FEBRUARY

I fell asleep on the damp grass beneath the wagon dreaming of a real home. I'd have Madame Adeline for my mother and Mr Marvel for my father and all the monkeys for my brothers and sisters. Mavis would be my special favourite, and would cuddle up with me every night in my safe, warm bed. I would eat pink cake and violet chocolates and sweet dates every day. I might perform on a little stage to earn my keep – an easy carpet act of somersaults and handstands – but my dear parents wouldn't hear of my attempting any springboard movements. It would be a solo act, no silver boys. Or perhaps it could be a double act with little Mavis.

DIAMOND

February 1

February 2

February 3

February 4

February 5

February 6

February 7

February 8

February 9

February 10

February 11

February 12

February 13

February 14

February 15

February 16

February 17

February 18

February 19

February 20

February 21

February 22

February 23

February 24

February 25

February 26

February 27

February 28

MY FEBRUARY DREAMS

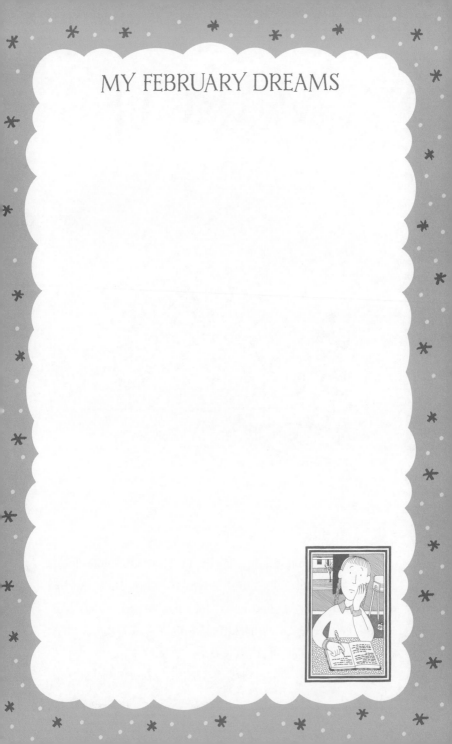

MARCH

We had to sing 'Happy Birthday' to Alisha, with Mrs Evans and Miss Suzanne conducting us. Then Alisha blew out her candles while her mother sprinkled her with sparkling confetti stuff. She said it was fairy dust and would make all Alisha's dreams come true.

THE WORST THING ABOUT MY SISTER

March 1

March 2

March 3

March 4

March 5

March 6

March 7

March 8

March 9

March 10

March 11

March 12

March 13

March 14

March 15

March 16

March 17

March 18

March 19

March 20

March 21

March 22

March 23

March 24

March 25

March 26

March 27

March 28

March 29

March 30

March 31

Notes

MY MARCH DREAMS

APRIL

'Oh Nan,' I said. 'Yes, dream about me! I know, we'll both dream, and then it'll be like we're really seeing each other. Let's dream tonight that we're going down the park and feeding the ducks together.'

QUEENIE

April 1

April 2

April 3

April 4

April 5

April 6

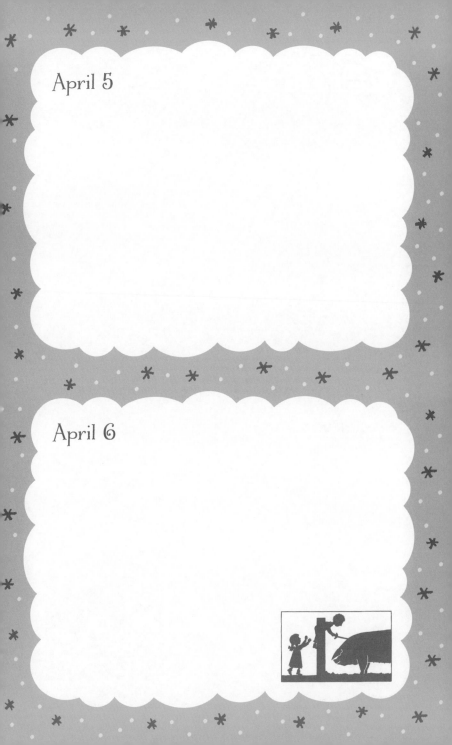

April 7

April 8

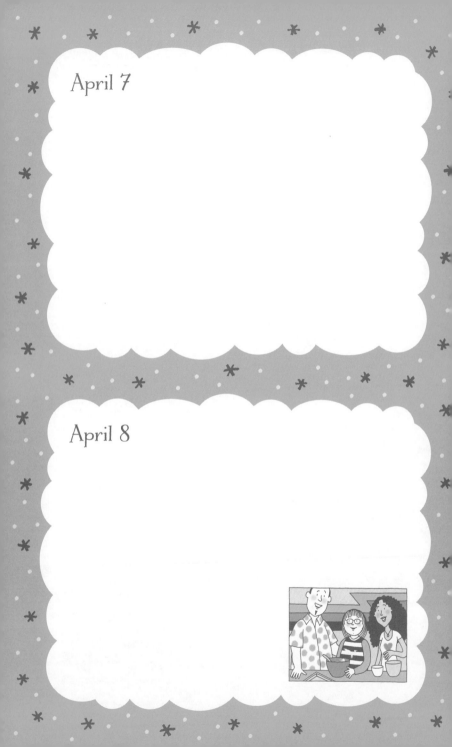

April 9

April 10

April 11

April 12

April 13

April 14

April 15

April 16

April 17

April 18

April 19

April 20

April 21

April 22

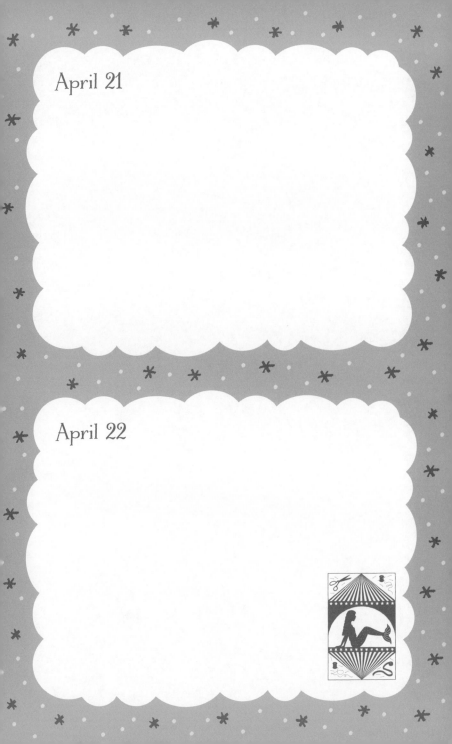

April 23

April 24

April 25

April 26

April 27

April 28

April 29

April 30

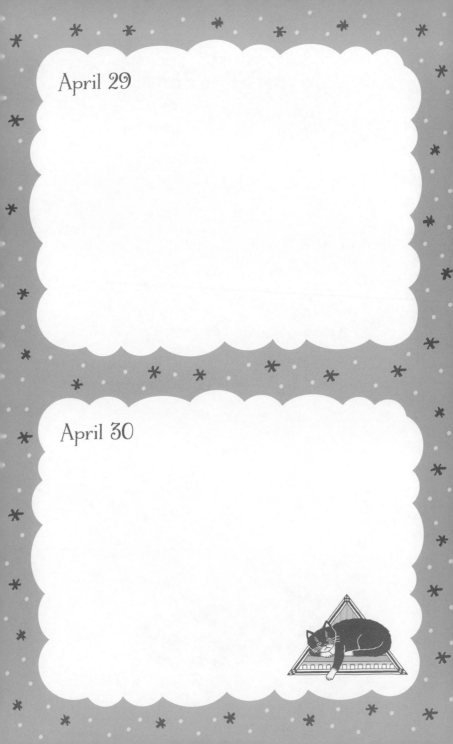

MY APRIL DREAMS

MAY

I wonder if she remembers me? If only I could remember her! I have these dreams where someone's lifting me up and holding me close and kissing me. Cathy's got a dream journal and writes all her dreams down.

DUSTBIN BABY

May 1

May 2

May 3

May 4

May 5

May 6

May 7

May 8

May 9

May 10

May 11

May 12

May 13

May 14

May 15

May 16

May 17

May 18

May 19

May 20

May 21

May 22

May 23

May 24

May 25

May 26

May 27

May 28

May 29

May 30

May 31

Notes

MY MAY DREAMS

JUNE

'Floss?'

Dad came stumbling out of his bedroom in his pyjamas and very nearly tripped over me. 'What are you doing here, pet? Don't cry. Come on, I'll take you back to bed. It's all right, Dad's here. You've just had a bad dream.'

CANDYFLOSS

June 1

June 2

June 3

June 4

June 5

June 6

June 7

June 8

June 9

June 10

June 11

June 12

June 13

June 14

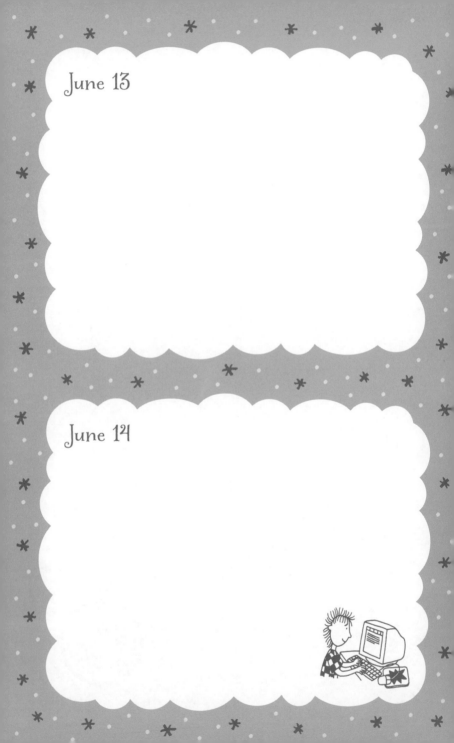

June 15

June 16

June 17

June 18

June 19

June 20

June 21

June 22

June 23

June 24

June 25

June 26

June 27

June 28

June 29

June 30

MY JUNE DREAMS

JULY

My absolute favourites were four enormous angels. They had long golden hair and flowing white robes and great grey wings springing from their shoulder blades. I stuck them in carefully, having to edge them in really close together to fit on the page. When I fell asleep I dreamed the angels were standing at each corner of our bed, wings spread out like feathery curtains protecting us.

LOLA ROSE

July 1

July 2

July 3

July 4

July 5

July 6

July 7

July 8

July 9

July 10

July 11

July 12

July 13

July 14

July 15

July 16

July 17

July 18

July 19

July 20

July 21

July 22

July 23

July 24

July 25

July 26

July 27

July 28

July 29

July 30

July 31

Notes

MY JULY DREAMS

AUGUST

Elaine is a pain but she's also quite quick at putting two and two together.

'Tracy, I don't think your mum will be coming today,' she said quietly.

'Oh. I know that. Only I had this dream. She did in the dream.'

'Yes, I'm sure she did. And I expect it was a lovely dream but—'

THE STORY OF TRACY BEAKER

August 1

August 2

August 3

August 4

August 5

August 6

August 7

August 8

August 9

August 10

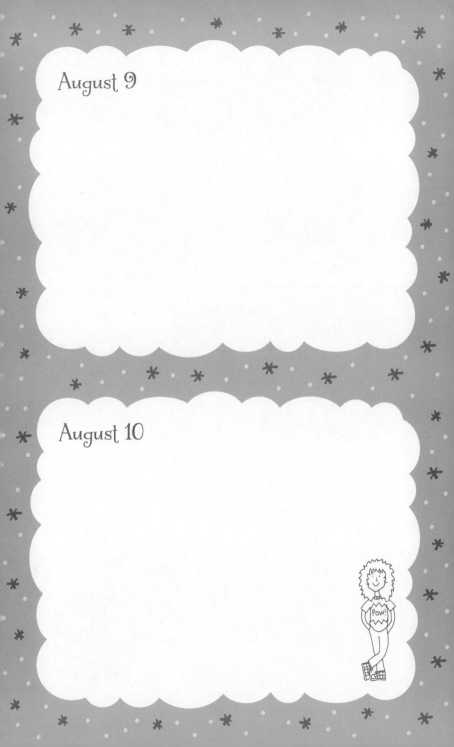

August 11

August 12

August 13

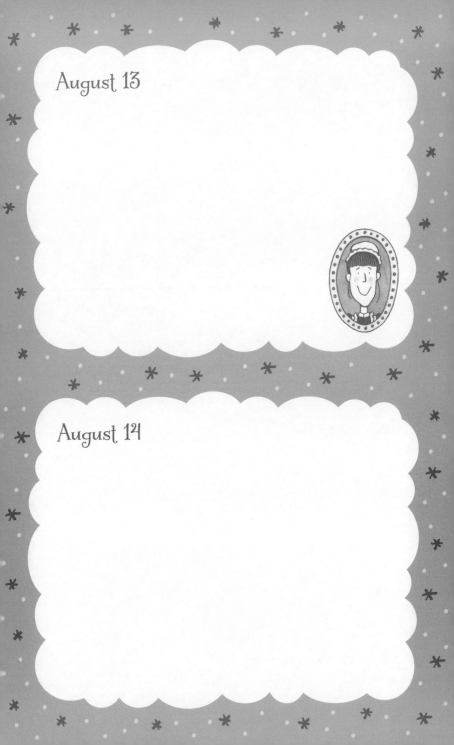

August 14

August 15

August 16

August 17

August 18

August 19

August 20

August 21

August 22

August 23

August 24

August 25

August 26

August 27

August 28

August 29

August 30

August 31

Notes

MY AUGUST DREAMS

SEPTEMBER

I couldn't be sure I wasn't making it all up. I closed my eyes, counted to three, and opened them again. Rabbit Cove was still there, serenely beautiful.

'I'm so pleased it's lovely,' said Mum. 'I was hoping and hoping it would be and yet sure it would be this ropy old pebbly place, all grey and ugly.'

'Maybe I'm still dreaming?' I said. 'And you're dreaming it too, Mum.'

'Well, let's park the car and then we'll have a little run on the beach. If you can feel the sand between your toes you're definitely wide awake,' said Mum.

COOKIE

September 1

September 2

September 3

September 4

September 5

September 6

September 7

September 8

September 9

September 10

September 11

September 12

September 13

September 14

September 15

September 16

September 17

September 18

September 19

September 20

September 21

September 22

September 23

September 24

September 25

September 26

September 27

September 28

September 29

September 30

MY SEPTEMBER DREAMS

OCTOBER

I cuddled up close to Hetty, and although I tried hard to keep my eyes open, I found I kept drifting off into dreams. I thought I was back in the big top, jumping on the springboard and then tumbling through the air, missing the boys altogether, crashing down, down, down into the sawdust. I woke, crying, and Hetty always hushed me tenderly.

DIAMOND

October 1

October 2

October 3

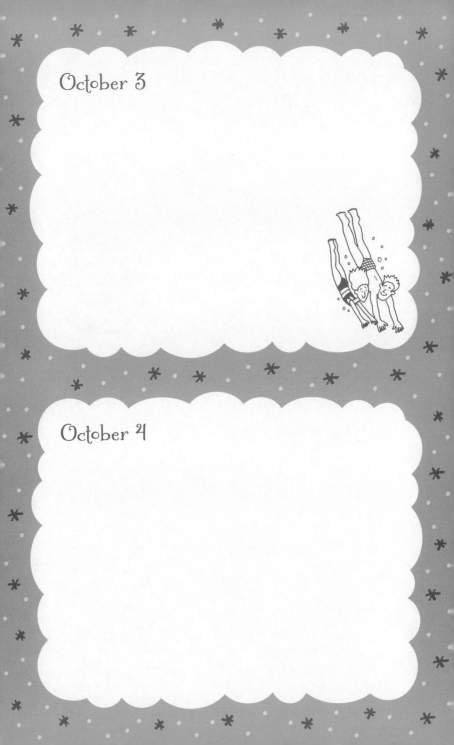

October 4

October 5

October 6

October 7

October 8

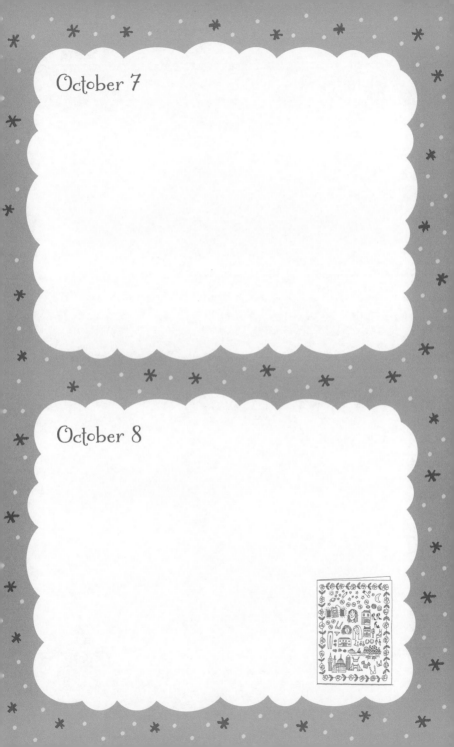

October 9

October 10

October 11

October 12

October 13

October 14

October 15

October 16

October 17

October 18

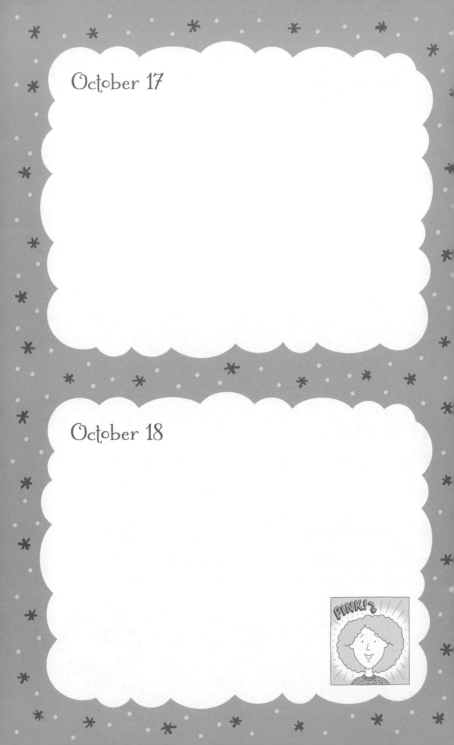

October 19

October 20

October 21

October 22

October 23

October 24

October 25

October 26

October 27

October 28

October 29

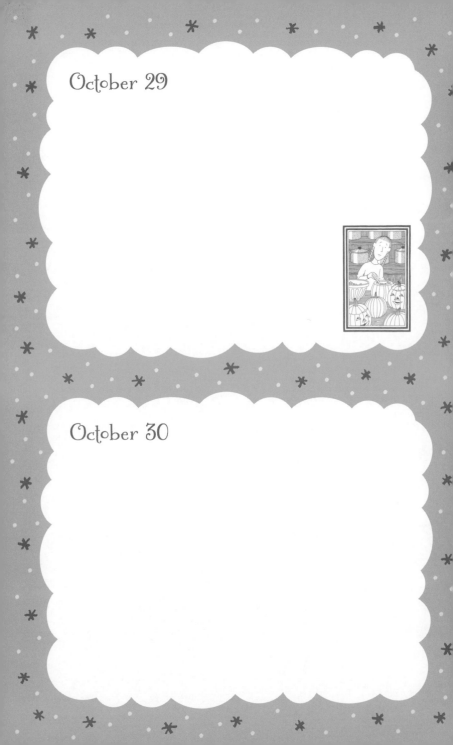

October 30

October 31

Notes

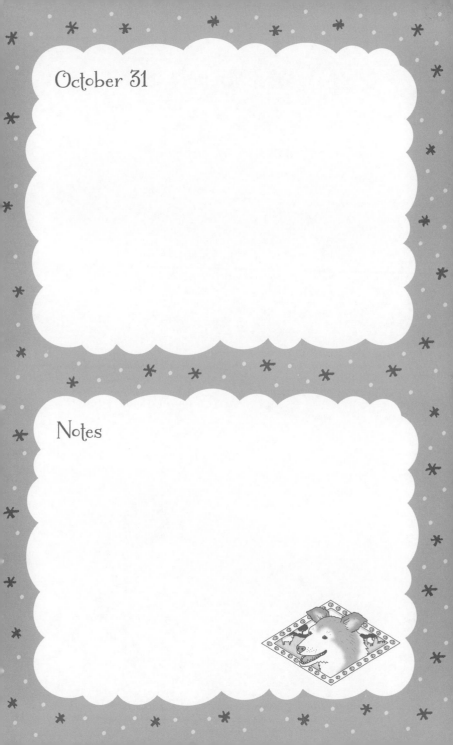

MY OCTOBER DREAMS

NOVEMBER

I was still trying to think of nine planets. I hadn't really been concentrating when we'd studied them at school. I'd been too busy dreaming up my own planet. Bluebell and I lived there all alone in perfect peace. There'd be hardly any gravity on Planet Dixie so I could fly just like Bluebell. We shared a special mossy nest at the top of the tallest tree. It bore multifruit all the year round, apples on one branch, pears on another. Raspberries and blackberries and strawberries grew in leafy clumps around the trunk and grape vines dangled downwards, so that we didn't have to leave our nest to peck at breakfast.

THE DIAMOND GIRLS

November 1

November 2

November 3

November 4

November 5

November 6

November 7

November 8

November 9

November 10

November 11

November 12

November 13

November 14

November 15

November 16

November 17

November 18

November 19

November 20

November 21

November 22

November 23

November 24

November 25

November 26

November 27

November 28

November 29

November 30

MY NOVEMBER DREAMS

DECEMBER

I went to sleep straight away. But then I started dreaming. It was like all the dinosaurs jumped straight off the duvet down my ear into my brain. I had a beautiful sleek special dinosaur friend but she suddenly bounded away into the woods and I couldn't find her any more. I was so lonely without her. I listened hard for her own special roar but I never heard it. So I made friends with some of the small dinosaurs.

THE ILLUSTRATED MUM

December 1

December 2

December 3

December 4

December 5

December 6

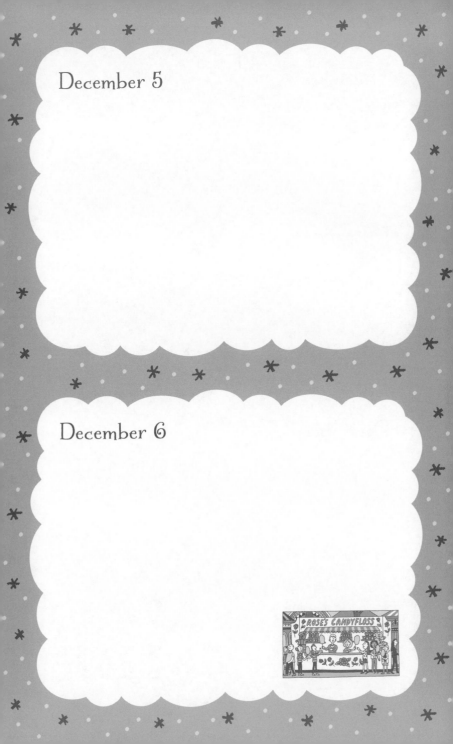

December 7

December 8

December 9

December 10

December 11

December 12

December 13

December 14

December 15

December 16

December 17

December 18

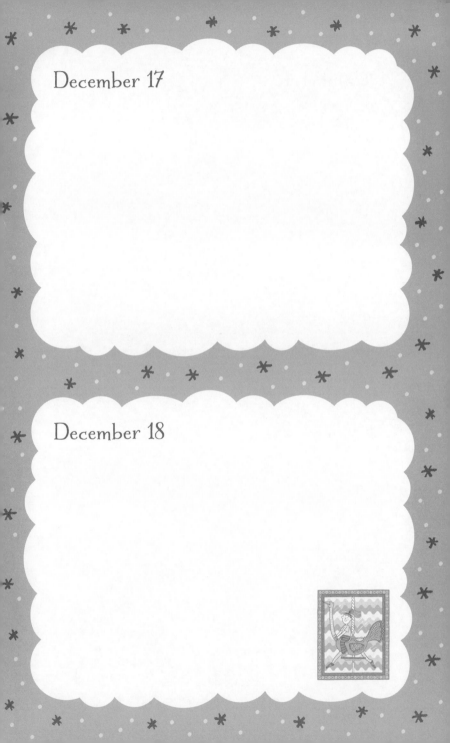

December 19

December 20

December 21

December 22

December 23

December 24

December 25

December 26

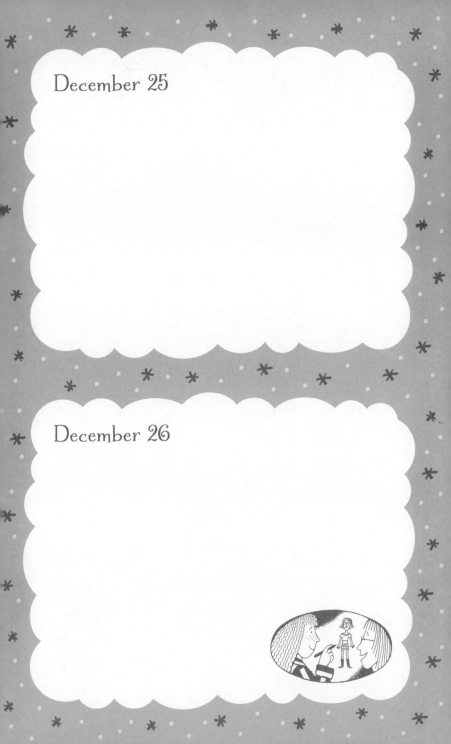

December 27

December 28

December 29

December 30

December 31

Notes

MY DECEMBER DREAMS

Be inspired! Look back at
all the dreams you've
had this year and use them
as ideas to write a story.
Turn the page to start . . .

Have you seen this other gorgeous stationery?

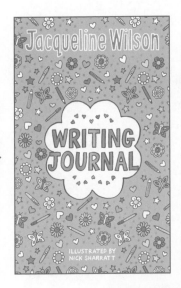

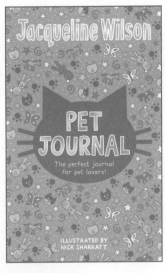

CHECK OUT
JACQUELINE WILSON'S
OFFICIAL WEBSITE!

There's a whole Jacqueline Wilson town to explore! You can generate your own special username, customise your online bedroom, test your knowledge of Jacqueline's books with fun quizzes and puzzles, and upload book reviews. There's lots of fun stuff to discover, including competitions, book trailers, and Jacqueline's scrapbook. And if you love writing, visit the special storytelling area!

Plus, you can hear the latest news from Jacqueline in her monthly diary, find out whether she's doing events near you, read her fan-mail replies, and chat to other fans on the message boards!

ALSO AVAILABLE BY JACQUELINE WILSON

THE JACQUELINE WILSON DREAM JOURNAL
A DOUBLEDAY BOOK ISBN 978 0 857 53431 6

First published in Great Britain by Doubleday,
an imprint of Random House Children's Publishers UK
A Random House Group Company

First Doubleday edition published 2005
This edition published 2014

1 3 5 7 9 10 8 6 4 2

Text in this edition copyright © Jacqueline Wilson, 2014
Illustrations in this edition copyright © Nick Sharratt, 2014

The Random House Group Limited supports the Forest Stewardship Council® (FSC®), the leading international
forest-certification organisation. Our books carrying the FSC label are printed on FSC®-certified paper. FSC is the
only forest-certification scheme supported by the leading environmental organisations, including Greenpeace.
Our paper procurement policy can be found at www.randomhouse.co.uk/environment.

Set in Liam

RANDOM HOUSE CHILDREN'S PUBLISHERS UK
61–63 Uxbridge Road, London W5 5SA

www.randomhousechildren.co.uk
www.totallyrandombooks.co.uk
www.randomhouse.co.uk

Addresses for companies within The Random House Group Limited can be found at:
www.randomhouse.co.uk/offices.htm

THE RANDOM HOUSE GROUP Limited Reg. No. 954009

A CIP catalogue record for this book is available from the British Library.

Printed and bound in China

PUZZLE ANSWERS

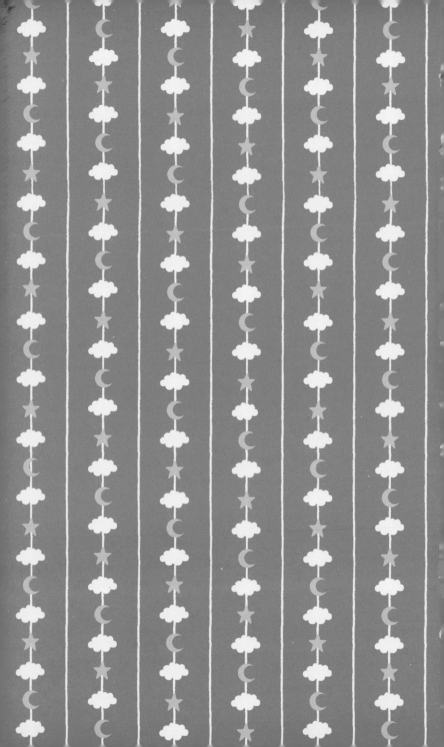